WORRY

You're three steps away from fixing it for good

Worry Box | Chapter One

FACE IT
FIX IT
FORGET IT

No worry on earth can stand up to the FFF solution!

Each of these three chapters helps you beat a particular sort of anxiety and you work on one topic at a time.

FACE IT (Chapter 2)

This chapter helps you FACE your fears and worries, stop avoiding things, and get some confidence and fun back into your life.

FIX IT (Chapter 3)

This chapter teaches you a foolproof way to FIX the problems you're worrying about - even the really tough ones.

FORGET IT (Chapter 4)

This chapter will help you FORGET those worrying thoughts that seem to take over and go round and round in your head.

Which chapter comes first?

IT DEPENDS WHAT SORT OF WORRY YOU DO MOST

If there's something you're scared of, that you're actively avoiding, like certain difficult situations or people, then facing your fear is a good place to start.

Read the pages in this chapter about FACE IT and then read the whole FACE IT chapter as well. It starts on page 25.

Alternatively, if there's a big problem in your life that you know is causing most of your worries, you might want to begin by fixing it.

Read the pages in this chapter about FIX IT, then read the whole FIX IT chapter as well (starting on page 47).

Or, if you're lying awake every night worrying about things (the world situation, so many responsibilities, too many demands on your time, other people's problems, mistakes or attitudes), you need to forget them, at least for a few hours, so that you can get some sleep.

Read the pages in this section about FORGET IT and then read the whole FORGET IT chapter as well. That's from page 71 onwards.

Are you ready to FACE IT?

FACE IT

Don't be fooled by feeling safe

When you're scared of something, you avoid it.

Sounds fair enough, doesn't it? Why volunteer to deliver a presentation if you don't like attention? Why go to a party if you don't feel comfortable in noisy, busy situations.

Trouble is, avoiding things doesn't fix them. Although not everyone wants to be in the limelight or loves parties, being frightened of things like this, can stop you enjoying some of the good things life offers.

So, worrying about busy places can lead to other outdoor trips becoming scary and you may find that you're staying in too much.

Avoidance can take other forms too. Some people are tempted to lean on drugs or alcohol to cope, others put things off they don't like again and again. All of this is avoidance.

Or we may fall into patterns of responding that make us feel safer at the time, but in the long-term backfire and reduce our confidence even more. Things like seeking reassurance from others, or hiding away in the corner.

Although these things make you feel more confident, it's a confidence trick. Truth is, they fool you into letting your fears have the upper hand, so that you do less and less and your life grows smaller and smaller.

What you need to do is call their bluff.

FACE IT

Stand up to the thing you're scared of

Think about one of the things you avoid doing. Do other people seem able to do it? Can you imagine yourself doing it, and how much better your life would be if you could?

Visualising the end goal of where you want to be might seem exciting. But it often is far too big a step to get there in one go.

Instead, think about a series of small steps you could take to build up your confidence and get you on the path to where you want to be.

Write down each of these steps (there's a page for this in the FACE IT chapter) and decide on what day and at what time you're going to take the first one. It's just a tiny step, remember, so it may simply involve opening the front door, looking up a phone number or any other small step that helps get you started.

Then, take that first step, and give yourself a pat on the back - you're at the beginning of the end of your fear!

> **This is just a taste of FACE IT. The full programme is in the FACE IT chapter (page 25).**

FIX IT

End the problem, end the worry

If you know what's wrong, you're already on the way to fixing it.

For example, if you're worrying because you have too much on, or about a relationship, completing an assignment or tidying the house, making a plan to tackle at least one thing will be a good start.

Fix the particular problem and you can stop worrying about it.

Often you don't even have to fix the problem, you just have to make *a plan* to fix the problem. Your mind will love the idea that you know what to do, and will stop being anxious and start being helpful.

But how do you make a plan? What if your problem is so huge that you can't even see where to start?

That's when you need to think about climbing a wall…

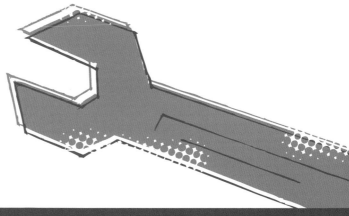

FIX IT

Imagine your problems are like having to get up a huge climbing wall. It's very high, and it seems a long haul to the top. How would you start? Take a running jump at the wall and try and hold on as far up it as possible? Or, take it a step at a time?

Problems are the same. To overcome them you need a plan:

1. Break your large problem into small chunks.

2. Tackle one at a time.

It's the same with any problem. No matter how big it seems, you can solve it by breaking it up into smaller chunks and working on one at a time. It might take ages, but you'll get there in the end, and your worry will often ease along with your problem.

Start by using our Easy Four Step Plan (E4SP for short):

Step 1 - break your problem into chunks
You can do anything if it's broken into small enough pieces*.

Step 2 - think of creative ways to tackle the first chunk
Take one of the little pieces and make a list of the different ways you might do it.

Step 3 - choose an idea and make a plan
Make sure your plan is small, practical and achievable.

Step 4 - check the plan and put it into action
Is your plan clear and realistic? Then Go for It!

* Did you read about the man who ate his car- really! - We don't recommend it.

This is just a taste of the Easy 4-Step Plan, the full programme is explained in the FIX IT chapter (page 47).

FORGET IT

Label it leave it Stand up to it Give yourself a break Look at it differently

Train your mind to master anxious thoughts

Do you have so many worries that you can't imagine fixing them all? Is there so much to be anxious about that you feel panicky, terrified or overwhelmed?

All these worries churning round in your head are just thoughts that have a bad impact on you. You can beat them with the ABTBP (Amazing Bad-Thought-Busting Programme).

When you notice a bad thought:

1. LABEL IT
Oh it's just one of those bad thoughts.

2. LEAVE IT
A bad thought loves attention, so don't give it any.

3. STAND UP TO IT
Bad thoughts are like bullies – weak underneath. You can face them.

4. GIVE YOURSELF A BREAK
What words of encouragement would someone who really loved you say? Trust them and let them help you beat the bad thought.

5. LOOK AT IT DIFFERENTLY
Give yourself the advice you'd give to a friend. Ask yourself if it will matter in six months.

Pick someone you respect and work out how they would handle the situation. Trust the facts, not the bad feelings.

There's much more about the ABTBP in the FORGET IT chapter (page 71).

FORGET
IT

Get up, it'll help you sleep

linked worksheet www.llttf.com/worksheets

If your bad thoughts are keeping you awake nights, you can beat them by creating a calm, half-hour space for yourself before bedtime. No caffeine or energy drinks, tea or coffee, no exercise, no eating, nothing that stimulates. Have a warm bath and a milky drink instead.

Don't read in bed or watch TV. Bed is for sleep- it's not the place for gaming, phones or social media.

When you're ready, settle down to sleep. If you find yourself tossing and turning, with worries going round and round in your head for more than fifteen minutes, get up and find this book.

Take one of the *Worry Strips* which are printed at the end of the book, copy it or cut it out. If you are reading this book online, print off the *'worry strips' worksheet*, or if you don't have a printer, copy what it says on the *Worry Strips* onto some paper or your phone.

Write down one thing that's worrying you on each strip and give each one a day and a time when you'll focus on sorting it out.

You might write: *Falling behind at work - Monday 5 pm* on one of them, and *Worried about a social media post - Thursday 1 pm* on another.

Do this until you have a number of slips, with worries, days and times on them. Look at all the completed strips and promise yourself that you're going to think about each problem on the day and time you've written down *but not until then.*

Now place the strips next to your Worry Box book and go to bed. You have nothing on your worry schedule at the moment, so get some sleep!

This is just a taste of FORGET IT, the full programme is in the FORGET IT chapter (page 71).

THE CHAPTERS WILL HELP YOU, BUT YOU'VE GOT TO HELP YOURSELF TOO

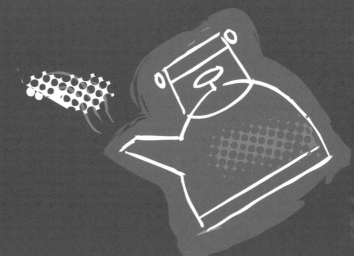

When you start this course, don't just skim through it, read it over and over again, make notes, draw diagrams, make plans and do other things that will help you get to the other side of your problem.

Stuff like this…

Put the kettle on or get some juice

Choose a time and place each day to read the content. Make it a quiet, comfy place, but not too relaxing. Have water, juice or a hot drink to sip while you're working. And make sure you have a pen and a notebook or paper.

Watch the snacks, no biscuits

Food can be a distraction. Just go to your reading place, close the windows, switch off the TV, the radio, the PC and the phone and concentrate on your learning.

Use weekly reviews

Get a diary and mark the start of your programme. Now, mark time for a Review Day on the same day every week for three months ahead. Once a week, on your Review Day, think about how you're doing. Then, if things are flagging, plan ways of getting back on track.

Stick up some sticky notes

Write messages on them about why you want to change and how great you're going to feel when it's done. Now stick them where you'll see them every day. And then, once a week, move them around so you don't get so used to them that you take no notice.

More ways to make the book work better

Don't do this alone
Tell some of the people you trust what you're doing and ask for their support.

They'll be there for you when you struggle, or when doubts set in. Call them up and tell them how you feel.

Give yourself some advice
Imagine it's not you with the problem, but your best friend who is finding things difficult.

What would you say to encourage your friend and remind him or her that things will be better when the problem is sorted? Now say that to yourself.

Think like an athlete
Top sports people don't win alone. They look for a great coach, good advice and get help in every way they can.

Like an athlete, you're aiming for results. The more help you get, the more chance you have of achieving them.

Write yourself a letter
Imagine it's ten years from now and you're sitting down to write a thank you letter to yourself.

Life is great - so much better than it used to be - and you want to thank the person you were ten years ago for creating such a better future.

What would you write? Read the letter in your head or write it down and keep a copy with you on your phone or set it up as a recurrent appointment so you remind yourself of it every day.

Ready to start? Time for Chapter 2... **Good Luck!**

FACE IT

Stand up to the things you're scared of

Worry Box | Chapter Two

FIRST, LET'S WORK OUT WHAT YOU WANT TO WORK ON

We all avoid things all the time. Broccoli, homework, walking mud into the house, tidying the house, even opera.*

In fact, life would be pretty strange if we didn't make choices about what we like and dislike, or what could have bad consequences for us.

But what if an opera singer avoided opera? This would probably affect his or her life, work and happiness, wouldn't it?

It's the same with everyday things. If someone was so nervous of going into busy shops that she avoided them, this would affect her life and happiness.

If someone avoided riding the bus because he hated traffic, that would affect his ability to get about. If someone avoided going to parties because he wasn't confident meeting people, that would affect his happiness and ability to make new friends.

So what about you: *what are you so worried about that you avoid it?*

*with apologies to opera fans and broccoli lovers

Turn over and make a list

27

My life, time with others or happiness would be better if I wasn't so worried about...

(we've filled in some examples)

Meeting new people. Being near animals. Being in crowded places.
Walking somewhere I might fall.
Giving a talk. Singing in public.

Now, write your own list here:

*Good list!
Now let's talk
about a con.*

DON'T BE FOOLED BY FEELING SAFE

Some people are scared of going out unless they're carrying their mobile phone. Others will only go shopping with family or friends.

Some constantly check things again and again before giving that presentation.

Although these things make us feel safer and more confident, it's a confidence trick. What they're doing is hiding the fact that they're scared.

For example, going shopping with friends might seem like a perfectly normal thing to do, but if it's hiding the fact that we're scared of shopping alone, we need to fix it.

Now: think about what you do and how you to do it, and work out whether any confidence tricks apply to you. If they do, turn back to your list and add these things to it.

To help you work out what else might be going on, some of the more common confidence tricks are on the next two pages.

WORRIED?
SCARED?
DRINK
ME

THE THINGS WE DO THAT HIDE OUR FEARS

Meeting new people. Being near animals. Being in crowds. Giving a talk. Singing in public. walking somewhere I might fall.

☐ **Checking**
This is when you keep checking if you switched the lights off or sent an email, or when you hate uncertainty so much that you really have to know how people have responded to your post on social media.

☐ **Clinging**
This is when you're always looking to others for approval, answers, reassurance or help. When you feel you couldn't manage if someone wasn't there for you.

☐ **Doing**
This is when you're busy, busy, busy, filling your life with work, activities and chores so that there's no time to do or think about the thing you're scared of.

☐ **Floating**
This is when you feel like you're not really connected to what's happening - as if you're floating above things, or as if you've made a 'box' for yourself that keeps the rest of the world out.

☐ **Hiding**
This is when you clam up or shrink into a corner at parties or meetings. You feel as if the only way to cope is by blending into the background.

☐ **Leaning**
This is when you lean on other people to get through a stressful situation.

☐ **Shouting**
This is when you hide your worries by getting angry or being frustrated at what other people say or do.

☐ **Taking**
This is when you sometimes see people use drink, drugs or cigarettes to get through something scary and to give false courage.

Do you do any of these things? If so, think about what they are hiding, and add those fears to your list.

LOOK AT THE LIST YOU MADE AND CHOOSE ONE THING TO WORK ON

Make it one of the less scary items - there are no prizes for jumping in the deep end.

Now ask two questions about the thing you've chosen:

1. Is it an everyday thing that most other people seem to do quite easily?

2. Can you imagine yourself doing it (and surviving) for just a short time?

If the answer is 'yes' to both questions, you've picked a good one to work on, so go to the end of this book or visit www.llttf.com/worksheets and make a copy of the *FACE IT Planner sheet.* If you are reading this book online print off the FACE IT Planner worksheet. No printer? Just write down what the FACE IT Planner says onto some paper or your phone.

Got it? Next in the **CAN'T** box at the top of the sheet, write down the thing you've decided to work on. Write the same thing in the **CAN** box at the bottom of the sheet.

If you need more FACE IT Planner sheets, you can print them for free at www.llttf.com/worksheets

Are you ready?

GOOD NEWS!

You've already started to make changes

Stage 1 is where you use the FACE IT Planner to write down what you want to work on.

What you're going to do, with the help of the FACE IT Planner and this little book, is go from **CAN'T** to **CAN** in 10 easy stages, working your way towards facing the thing you're avoiding, and tackling it.

Now it's time for stage 2 - the plan. Read the next couple of pages and make a plan to slowly work through the steps of the FACE IT Planner until you have actually done the thing you're scared of.

There's an example later.

PLAN TO FACE YOUR FEARS

The key is to take it a step at a time. You can handle the scariest things in the world if you don't have to jump right in. So think about your goal and the slow, steady steps you'd take to reach it.

For example:

Chloe used to like shopping but she was ill and missed work for a while, and since then, has been anxious about going into busy shops by herself.

This is what she wrote in her plan for changing **CAN'T** go shopping to **CAN** go shopping.

1. Go into town and walk past the shops with no intention of going inside.

2. Walk past the shops again and stop outside until I notice my anxiety starts to drop. This may take 15 minutes or more.

3. Repeatedly, stop outside the shops for at least 20 minutes or longer until my anxiety levels fall.

4. Go into the shop and just stay by the door for 15 minutes or more, until the anxiety levels reduce again. If that's too much, start with a few minutes and work from there. If I feel really bad, leave, but not quickly.

5. Repeatedly go in again, deeper into the shop, for at least fifteen minutes or longer until my anxiety levels fall.

6. Pick different sizes of shop, with more and less people inside. The next steps on the FACE IT sheet are where I shop again and again until I've built my confidence at each step, and my anxiety has reduced to a level that feels comfortable.

My aim is to be able to shop in any type of shop, however busy without feeling scared.

Chloe knew she could take one step a day, or one step a week, it didn't matter. What mattered was having a plan and making steady progress toward **CAN**.

That was Chloe's example. Now it's your turn.

Getting from CAN'T to CAN

Think about the little steps you can take in your FACE IT Planner. Make them really small - so they build up over time. And don't worry if you have to keep crossing things out, there's plenty of space.

Write them here. You might need to have a short version to fit them in the boxes.

CAN'T

1 Visualise my goal - *Done*

2 Make my plan - *You're doing this now*

3 First I'm going to...

4 Next I'm going to...

5 Then I'm going to...

6

7

8

9

10

CAN

Well planned!

WHAT IF SOMETHING GETS IN THE WAY?

As soon as you've written your plan, think about what could stop it happening. Are there any things that might trip you up? What about other people? Could someone be unhelpful at any stage?

Are you tempted to have a drink, or offer a ready-made excuse to get out of the situation? If so try to face your fear without them. See page 33 for a full list of things we do to hide our fears.

You can change how you feel by changing what you do.

When you've worked out what could block your progress, make another mini-plan for getting round the obstacle. It's called **unblocking.**

This way, you'll be ready for whatever happens!

Now check your plan

Is it realistic?

There are no prizes for jumping straight into the deep end.

Are you aiming at just one thing?

Don't try and do more than one item on your list at the same time. You can always pick another when you've sorted the first one.

Is it slow?

There's no need to rush at things. Your plan can take as long as you like, so long as you stick to it, step by step.

Is it easy?

Make your steps small and easy and you'll be more likely to do them.

Are you ready to unblock it?

Have you thought about what could go wrong and how to deal with it?

FIVE TICKS?
THEN GO FOR IT!

BUT WHAT IF I GET STUCK?

If you find that you're struggling halfway through, just sit down and think about why –

• Are the steps too big or difficult?

• Am I pushing for change too quickly?

• Do you need to predict what might get in the way- and how to tackle any problems?

• Would it have been better if you had chosen something else on your list?

If the steps are feeling really difficult now, go back to your plan and rewrite it to make the next few steps smaller and easier.

Now, run on the spot

If you're getting stuck on a particular step, take a step back and repeat the last step you managed to get to. Don't try to make progress to the next stage yet, just keep on repeating the current one, until your confidence builds up and you can start to go forward again. You need a next step that moves your forward, but isn't such a big step it seems too hard.

Watch out for hiding

As you plan to make changes, you need to also plan to reduce the activities you do that hide your fears (checking, clinging, doing, floating, hiding, leaning, shouting, or taking - see page 33).

So, if you get stuck again, make a mini-plan to unblock the problem. And remember, the mini-plan must have small, easy steps.

And if you really can't continue with this plan, don't give yourself a hard time, look at your *FACE IT Planner* and give yourself a pat on the back for having got this far.

Keep your plan in a safe place (you'll need it when you go back to this plan in the future) and choose another item from your list.

Time for Chapter 3...

WORRY
B□X

FIX IT
End the problem,
end the worry

Worry Box | Chapter Three

Too much to do

No Money

Got bullied

Social media post backfired

We broke up

Being ill

Failed an exam

Lost my job

Best friend ignored me

Got criticised

Someone close is really poorly

Can you trace your worries back to one big thing?

Is there one big worry on your mind?

Maybe it's like a cloud that's hanging over you, making bright days dull and spoiling things that should be fun?

GOOD NEWS!

PROBLEMS ARE SOMETHING YOU CAN TACKLE

If you're facing just one big problem in your life, you don't have to work directly on the worry it causes, all you have to do is fix the problem that's causing it. The money problem, the friend problem, the exam problem, the too much work to do problem.

If you're saying to yourself "Don't you think I'd have done it by now if I knew how to fix the problem?" we understand.

So by the end of this chapter, we're confident that you *will* know how to fix the problem.

What's more, you'll already be worrying about it less, because we all feel better when we have a plan.

The first step in solving a problem, any problem, is to cut it down to size - to break it into tiny little chunks that, by themselves, are easy to do.

Then you work out how you're going to do each chunk, make a plan, and carry it out. It's called the Easy 4-Step Plan (E4SP for short) and it really works.

It will help you get to the top of a climbing wall, climb a mountain- or tackle any problem.

HOW DO YOU GET TO THE TOP?

a. Remember, you get to the top by taking a series of small steps

b. Take each step one at a time

Problems are like climbing walls. They seem overwhelming and sometimes scary.

But when you break the problem of getting to the top into small chunks, it's much less frightening and a lot easier to achieve.

STEP 1:

Break your problem into chunks

Let's say you need to revise for a professional exam. You could create a timetable and cover each topic one per day.

If you're spending too much, you could start by cutting out online shopping.

If you have too much work to do, take just one piece of work and make a plan to do it.

Most tasks can be chunked like this and we're going to practice doing it later.

Meantime, turn over for step 2 of the E4SP

STEP 2: THINK OF CREATIVE WAYS TO TACKLE THE FIRST CHUNK

Take a piece of paper and write down all the things you could do to work on the first bit of the chunk - planning that first step.

To revise for a professional exam, you could focus on one area of your topic first, and go on the internet to do some research tomorrow evening.

Trying to cut down online shopping? Use the parental controls in your browser to lock yourself out of the sites you spend money on.

To get your work done, put your phone on airplane mode and plan to do at least some of it before eating each night.

Stuck for ideas? Work out what advice you'd give a friend who is trying to sort out the same problem. Think about other people in the same situation - what have they done?

Step 3 next.

STEP 3: CHOOSE AN IDEA AND MAKE A PLAN TO DO IT

Look at your ideas and pick one. Choose one that doesn't scare you too much.

Now take another piece of paper and write down, step by step, how to actually *do* it.

Make the steps as small as you like:

Write a *To Do* list - and which day you'll start on the first task.

OR

To revise history today, get your textbook and read the chapter covering the topic you are learning. Plan to look up more information tomorrow online.

OR

For online shopping: open your browser. Go to Tools. Go to security settings. Add shopping sites to the restricted zone (or whatever variation of this you need to do on your particular software).

Make sure that the steps are small, practical and seem like things you could really do.

What if something gets in the way?

As soon as you've written your plan, think about what could stop it happening. Is there anything that might trip you up? What about other people? Could someone be unhelpful at any stage? Watch out for doing things that help you hide (page 33).

When you've worked out what might block your progress, make another mini-plan for getting round the obstacle so that you're ready for whatever happens.

Final step coming up.

STEP 4.
CHECK
THE PLAN AND
PUT IT INTO
ACTION

This is it! You have a plan, now you need to check that it's going to work.

Use this checklist:

Is it realistic?

☐

Don't be over ambitious. Aim for a fun run rather than a marathon.

Are you aiming at just one thing?

☐

Fix one problem at a time. Only pick another from your list when you've sorted the first one.

Is it slow?

☐

There's no rush. Your plan can take as long as you like, so long as you stick to it, step by step.

Is it easy?

☐

Make your steps small and easy and you'll be more likely to do them.

Are you ready to unblock it?

☐

Have you thought about what could go wrong and how to deal with it?

FIVE TICKS? THEN GO FOR IT!

And that's how you fix any problem, even the enormous mountain sized ones.

Hiccup cure overleaf.

WHAT TO DO WHEN THE GOING GETS TOUGH

If you have a bit of a hiccup halfway through your plan (lots of us do), try these ideas to remind yourself why you started in the first place.

- Write down the reasons you want to do this and put them where you can see them.

- Think how you'll feel 2 or 3 weeks or months from now if you give in. Write that down and place your summary where you can see it.

- Tell as many supportive family or friends as possible what you're doing, so that they can help you (or encourage you when you slip).

- Think about the advantages of succeeding – you'll be less worried, you'll feel as if a weight has been lifted from your shoulders, you'll have better health, better relationships, more friends, more fun, more money. Write those down and put them where you can see them.

Ready for some practice?

If you're not sure how to apply the E4SP to your problem, the next four pages will help.

They show two real plans, created by people like you, to fix their problems and turn their lives around.

You'll see how to use this approach in practice, so you'll be clear what to do for your own plans, so it doesn't matter if the examples don't apply to you.

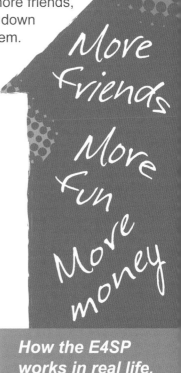

More friends

More fun

More money

How the E4SP works in real life.

I WANT TO MAKE NEW FRIENDS

STEP 1: Break your problem into chunks

How do you break 'making new friends' into little chunks? Change it to 'make one new friend'. It's a lot easier to work at finding and connecting with one person than to try to transform yourself into the life and soul of the party.

So let's say your chosen step is 'Find and make one new friend'. You can always repeat the process when you've succeeded.

STEP 2 : Think of creative ways to tackle the first chunk

Here's how your creative ideas might go:
- List the people you know already that you'd like to be a friend
- List the people who you haven't spoken to or hung out with for a while
- Stop eating alone in the cafeteria and sit with other people
- Ask people you know to introduce you to other people
- Join a club or society. If it involves sports or fitness, you could crack two problems at once!

STEP 3 : Choose an idea and make a plan to do it

Let's choose idea 1 (List the people you know already that you'd like to be a friend) and make a plan. Make a list of the people who you met briefly and those who you added on social media or swapped numbers with but have never contacted.

If you have no way of contacting them but you know their name, add them on your social media with a friendly message. Now take a look at those whose numbers you do have, and those who are already your online friends.

Choose one person and text or call them up, or send them an instant message. Invite them to study with you, go for coffee or go to a concert. If they are someone you know from work, ask them if you can borrow their notes or ask them a question about a difficult piece of work.

Repeat this process with the next person on your list.

STEP 4 : Check the plan and put it into action

Check the plan (see pages 58 and 59) and if you have 5 ticks, go for it. And remember, if this plan doesn't work out, or it gets too much for you in the middle, don't beat yourself up, just go back to Step 2, and pick another idea to try!

You can do it!

I NEED TO STUDY FOR EXAMS

Step 1 : Break your problem into chunks

Almost everyone is worried about exams and sometimes you can feel like a rabbit in the headlights - there's so much to do, so many subjects to study that you just can't get started.

This is where the step by step chunking idea is really handy - and really obvious. Don't try and study every-thing, just do one subject at a time. So your chunks could be: World War 1, World War 2, The Korean War etc. Let's say WW1 - that's Step 1.

Step 2 : Think of creative ways to tackle the first chunk

Your creative thinking of ways to study WW1 could come up with ideas like these:

- Make a list of the chapters you need to read and go through them one by one
- Make a timetable so that you cover everything by the exam
- Find a friend who's doing the same topic and work together in the library
- Divide your week into study periods and don't go out or watch TV at those times.
- Decide on three days a week for study and text your friends to say your phone will be off on those days.
- Work at a friend's house - but watch the chat and banter.
- Go to the library and get some books out about studying techniques.

Step 3 : Choose an idea and make a plan to do it

Let's say you choose idea 3 - find a friend and work together. This is what your plan could include.
- Call your friends in the same class, one by one, and outline your idea.
- Do a deal with the first one who agrees.
- Get together and decide on a day to start work
- Decide on a place to work
- Discuss the study methods you will use - testing each other?
- Have a plan for when motivation fades.
- Discuss and agree on a system of small rewards for good work. Maybe visit the cinema once a week.

Step 4: Check the plan and put it into action

Check your plan for 5 ticks (pages 58 and 59) and put it into action. And remember, you'll need motivation, especially when you've done the first couple of days and there's still a lot to cover, or something you don't like.

Here are some of the things you could stick on the wall of your study room to remind you why you're doing this:

Better exam results mean a better career and more money

Bad exam results mean little choice of what you do in life

Bad exam results only mean you'll have to do it all again next year

More people fail exams through not working

You'll feel great when you've done each subject and can reward yourself

A good performance may mean promotion and a chance to celebrate with family and friends.

You can do it!

65

NOW IT'S YOUR TURN!

My problem is:

STEP 1 – Break your problem into chunks

linked
worksheet
www.llttf.com/worksheets

STEP 2 – Think of creative ways to tackle the first chunk

Step 3 next.

STEP 3 – Choose an idea and make a plan
to do it

Step 4 - Check the plan and put it into action

Is it realistic?

Are you aiming at just one thing?

Is it slow?

Is it easy?

Are you ready to unblock it?

linked
worksheet
www.llttf.com/worksheets

Concentrate on fixing just one problem at the moment.

Tackle the problem one chunk at a time.

The Easy 4 Step Plan is a powerful tool that can be used to tackle any life problem.

You can download more E4SP planning sheets for free from llttf.com/worksheets.

GOOD LUCK!

Time for Chapter 4...

FORGET IT

Train your mind to master anxious thoughts

Worry Box | Chapter Four

A WORD ABOUT THOSE WORRIES IN YOUR HEAD

Do you sometimes feel overwhelmed? Does everything seem to get on top of you and there are just too many problems to face or fix?

Do you have worries about other people - what they're doing or thinking, or what might happen to them?

Maybe you're blaming yourself for something that's gone wrong, perhaps you're anxious that someone doesn't think much of you, or that you've said something to upset a friend or relative.

Although these kinds of worries can seem hard to shift, they'll fade away when you work with this FORGET IT chapter.

THIS CHAPTER IS IN TWO PARTS

First, you'll tackle your bad thoughts

It starts with the Amazing Bad Thought Busting Programme (ABTBP for short). This helps you see your worries for what they are: just bad thoughts that are trying to upset you.

Bad thoughts are the opposite of helpful thoughts. They don't solve problems or provide helpful ideas, they're completely useless. Sometimes, they turn up when we're feeling down but often they arrive uninvited and make us even more stressed out and fed up.

Soon, you'll be able to get rid of them.

Next, you'll fall asleep

The second half of the chapter helps you beat one of the biggest problems with worry - getting to sleep at night - and it also has a great new way to clear your head and start to solve your problems.

Let's begin by putting a name to some of the bad thoughts you're having.

Bad thought spotter this way.

BAD THOUGHT SPOTTER

Bad thoughts are also known as unhelpful thinking styles. If they pop into mind and stay there, they have a bad effect on how you feel emotionally, and on what you do. There's a list of the most common ones on the next page.

If you keep having any of these thoughts, make a note of them, or tick one or more of the boxes that you have noticed. It means you've spotted a bad thought that you can fix with the ABTBP.

BAD THOUGHT

Are you your own worst critic?
Do you always seem to be beating yourself up about something?

□

Do you focus on the bad stuff?
As if you were looking at the world through darkened glasses?

□

Do you have a gloomy view of the future?
Expecting everything to turn out badly?

□

Are you jumping to the very worst conclusions?
Taking things to extremes is called 'catastrophising'.

□

Do you assume that others see you badly?
When you haven't checked whether it's true- it's called 'mind-reading'.

□

Do you take responsibility for everything?
Including things that aren't your fault?

□

Are you always saying things like 'Should' 'Ought to' 'Got to'?
Setting impossible standards for yourself?

□

Turn over to write down your thoughts.

MY BAD THOUGHTS

Remembering a time when you felt bad, what went through your mind at the time?

Include thoughts or any mental pictures about yourself or about others, about what was happening or might happen, or about what other people might think of you.

Now step this way for
the ABTBP...

ABTBP Step 1

LABEL THE THOUGHT

When you notice one of your bad thoughts, don't get upset by them, instead just mentally step back and stick a label on it.

"Oh, that's just one of those bad thoughts"

When you label a bad thought this way, it loses its power and you realise that it's just part of being upset.

It's not the truth, it's just one of those bad thoughts.

You could even talk to it. Say: "You're spotted! I'm not playing that game again!"

LEAVE IT ALONE

Now you know what it is, mentally turn your back on the bad thought.

Don't challenge it or try to argue with it, just let it be.

A bad thought loves attention, so don't give it any.

Instead, think about what you're doing right now - really focus on this moment or on the conversation you may be having.

Keep doing what you're doing and don't get knocked off track.

Step 3 next.

ABTBP Step 3

STAND UP TO IT!

Don't be bossed about by bad thoughts. Bad thoughts are like bullies. They sound strong but really they're weak underneath. And they tell lies.

They say you won't like doing something. They say you'll fail if you try. They tell you you're rubbish or you're scared or nobody likes you.

But this is just the bad thought, not the truth. Don't be bullied!

If the thought says "Don't!" then DO!

If the thought says "Can't" say CAN! Right back at it.

Easy for us to say? You're right. But just give it a try, one time. You'll find that you really can beat bad thoughts.

linked
worksheet
www.llttf.com/worksheets

At first, you may still be tossing and turning, even after your warm bath and hot milky drink, so here's what you do:

Use the ABTBP to try and tackle the bad thoughts for about a quarter of an hour each night.

Label them, leave them, stand up to them, give yourself a break and look at things differently.

If you're still awake after that, get up, leave the bedroom and turn to the end of the book and make a copy of the *Worry Strip* or visit www.llttf.com/worksheets and print off the *Worry Strips*. You're going to sort those bad thoughts out – literally.

THE WORRY BOX

WRITE DOWN YOUR WORRIES AND PUT THEM AWAY

Sit down at a table and take the *Worry Strip* sheet.

Cut it into strips and write down one thing that's worrying you on each strip.

Just doing this - separating out each of the things you're worrying about - will help untangle them and make them easier to cope with.

Look at all the strips you've written on and decide whether any of the worries are ones that you could FACE or FIX.

If so, put the ones you could FACE into the FACE IT chapter, like a bookmark, and put the ones you could FIX into the FIX IT chapter.

Now you have them sorted, the next step is to plan a time to deal with them.

I'm worrying about...

Falling behind with work

I'll deal with it on Thursday at 1 pm

I'm worrying

They didn't speak to me today

I'll deal with it on Monday at 5 pm

What about the other worries?

WORKING OUT YOUR WORRY SCHEDULE

I think Emily is upset with me

on Thursday at 🕒 3 p.m.

Now, for each strip in turn, look at the squares on the end of each *Worry Strip* and give each worry a day and a time, from tomorrow onwards.

Your strips could say:

I think Emily is upset with me. Thursday 3 pm

and

I don't feel as if I'm appreciated by the team. Wednesday 6 pm.

Do this for all the worries until all the strips have thoughts, days and times on them.

Next, find a left-over box like a shoe box or similar. Write on the box – 'Worry Box', then get your scissors and cut a small hole through the lid so you can post your *Worry Strips* in the Worry Box. Now you have your own Worry Box - somewhere to post your worries to deal with later.

Look at the slips and promise yourself that you're going to think about each problem on the day you've written down *but not until then.*

Now post your completed *Worry Strip* through the slot in the top of your newly created Worry Box and go back to bed. You have nothing on your worry schedule at the moment, so you are officially entitled to get some rest!

Sleep tight.

Time for Chapter 5.

linked resource
www.lttf.com/
worksheets

To download the
Tension Control
Training MP3

MEET THE LIAR

Stay or go? Tough it out or phone a friend?

If, even after you've done the breathing exercise and remembered about adrenaline, you still feel bad, then do what you have to do, but do it slowly - don't rush away, don't gulp that drink down and don't make it an emergency

Alternatively, you could try something radical: stick it out!

Breathe calmly through your nose, think rationally and put those scary thoughts in their place.

If you're able to face your fear this way, proving to yourself, just a little bit each time, that the worst fears are not always true or helpful, you'll have taken a big step towards fixing your panic attacks for good.

There are some good long-term plans for tackling panic in all the sections in the Worry Box Resource.

Start reading them now, before your next panic attack.

If you need more help than this book can offer, try to talk to a person you trust or your own General Practitioner (GP) or other health care worker.

Some excellent information resources from respected health organisations and mental health charities are available online.

I'm worrying about...

worry strip

I'll deal with it on ___ at ___

I'm worrying about...

worry strip

I'll deal with it on ___ at ___

Permission is given to photocopy this page for use in your own life

I'm worrying about...

worry strip

I'll deal with it on [   ] at 🕘

I'm worrying about...

worry strip

I'll deal with it on [   ] at 🕘

FACE IT Planner

Visualise

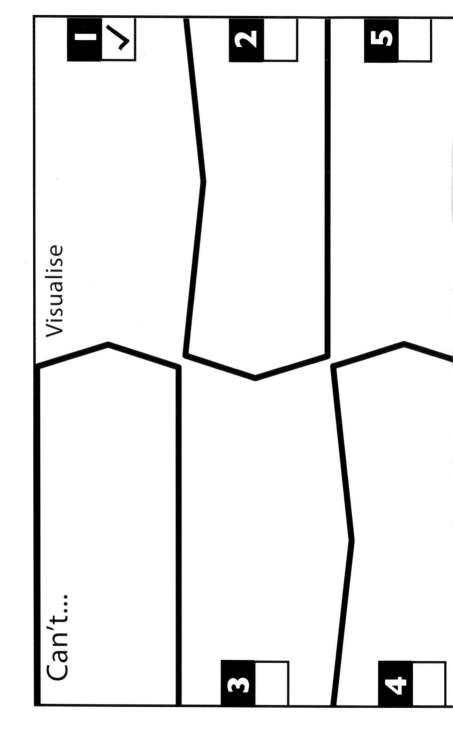

1 ✓

2

5

Can't...

3

4

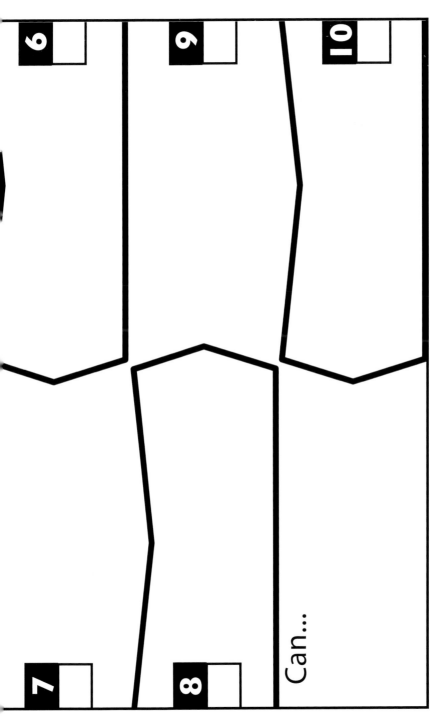

6

9

10

7

8

Can...

I'm worrying about...

I'll deal with it on [ ] **at** [ ]

worry strip

I'm worrying about...

I'll deal with it on [ ] **at** [ ]

worry strip

Permission is given to photocopy this page for use in your own life